MATTY'S ROCKET

BOOK ONE

DIESELFUNK

Presents

BOOK ONE

Created, Written
and illustrated by

TIM FIELDER

Copyright © 2022
Dieselfunk Studios, LLC
ISBN-13: 978-0-9962046-6-8

Dieselfunk Studios
www.dieselfunk.com

Ordering Information:
U.S. trade bookstores and
wholesalers, please email,
admin@dieselfunk.com

Quantity sales and discounts
are available on purchases by
corporations, associations, and
others. For details, contact the
publisher at the address above.

**Printed in the United States
of America**

INTRODUCTION

I want to thank my Parents; Arthur and Rowena Fielder, Siblings; Jim, Boston and Arthur, my Wife; Melanie, and my Kids; Johnnie Lee, Jacob, and Maximilius.

Tremendous respect and thanks to Steph Curry, Jeff Smith and Erika Hardison. This would not have happened without you. Thanks to Marc Florestant, Floyd Hughes, Junot Díaz, Dawud Anyabwile, John Jennings, Stacey Robinson, Joyce Brabner, Andre Peltier, Dr. Toneisha Taylor, Dr. Reynaldo Anderson, Ytasha Womack, Dr. Kinitra Brooks, Dr. Julian Chambliss, Debbie Mitchell, Ruth LaFerla, Keith Miller, Meredith Theeman, Kat Fajardo, Barbara Brandon-Croft, Sharon Lee De La Cruz, James Mason, and David Brame. Luther Smith, Steve Williams, Tracie Morris, Tarra Rhymes, Akwanza Gleaves, Darius James, DJ Venom, Greg Anderson Elysée, Jude Terror, Kadija George, and Dorothea Smartt for motivation. Special thanks to Jason and Kemi Reeves for their gracious handholding through the production of this book.

This book is Dedicated to the Women who brought me up: Ruby Young, Helen Lott, AV Hughes, Rowena Fielder, Myrna Delores Bain, Patricia Robinson, Harriet Tubman, Bessie Coleman and last but not least, My Great-Grandmother, Matty "Walking Stick" Watty.

Matty's Rocket would not exist without the Influential works of Samuel R Delany, Octavia Butler, Overton Lloyd, Shusei Nagoaka, Frank Hampson, Will Eisner, Philip Francis Nowlan, Alex Raymond, Lotte Reiniger, Wally Wood, Jean Giraud, Ron Cobb, Joe Johnston, Fritz Lang, Kara Walker, Bourne Hogarth, Brad Bird, Frank Kapra, Ralph McQuarrie, Oscar Micheaux, Jack Kirby, George Pal, Jerry Siegel, Joe Schuster, Richard Corben, Michael Golden, Tim Conrad and George Lucas.

M atty's Rocket is what I call Retro-Afrofuturism. I take the past and add in the future, but fill it with people of color. Matty has the blasters, the rockets, the spacesuits, and the hero still gets the girl, or boy. Most importantly of all...We LIVE.

With that, I welcome you to Matty's Rocket Book One.

ENJOY,

Tim Fielder

For Johnnie Lee

While we often have no words to heal the chasm between us, perhaps my images can bridge the difference.

This book, my Darling, is for You. It was always for YOU.

Daddy

1

MATTY'S ROCKET

Ready For Blastoff!

BIGHEAD SCIENTISTS

FIELDER

DIESELFUNK

MATTY'S ROCKET

Chapter 1

Ready For Blastoff

a BIGHEAD SCIENTISTS production

COAHOMA COUNTY, MISSISSIPPI
1920

I was first born Matty Delores Watty in a rickety cabin with green paint.

I remember the paint because it would chip off and scatter all over the yard.

You could almost say I was born twice in life.

I lived the life that many children of the Jim Crow South lived. Our elders made sure we knew the rules.

But still, we had our pleasures that only youthful ignorance could provide.

CASSEL, FRANCE
1938

Now, my second birthplace would be many thousands of miles away.

Like any Gal, I liked Speed.

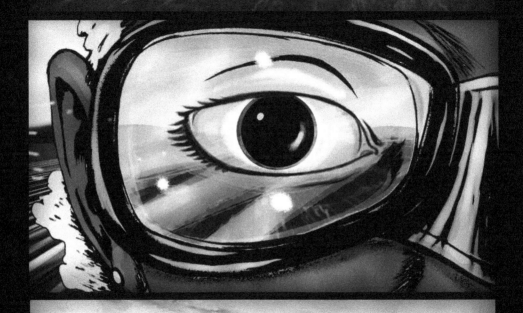

Well,...maybe I liked it a lot more than most.

I could'nt get the required license and training to fly rockets stateside.

Not one to take no for an answer, I found passage to a country that wouldn't let skin color get in the way.

As ready as
I'll ever be!

Francois helped me to find this rocket for a relatively cheap price.

With most of my savings blown, it felt like I spent a mint.

I'll never forget the rocket I took up for my test.

It was one of those older Strato-capsules used heavily in the Post Invasion.

10, 9,...

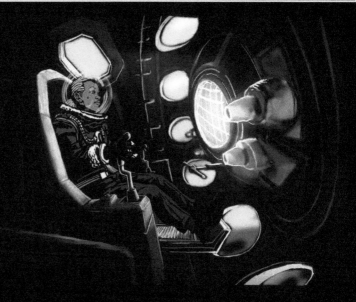

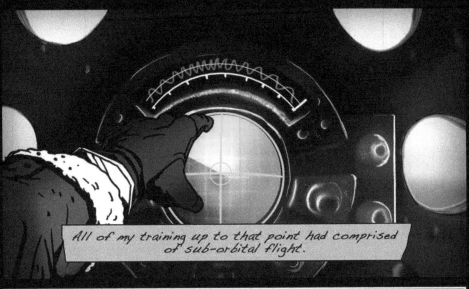

All of my training up to that point had comprised of sub-orbital flight.

8, 7,...

It was at this moment that I was reborn—
like a Phoenix or something.

6, 5, 4,...

This would be the real thing.

3, 2, 1,...

Ignition!

Although I often voiced my desire to be an acrobat, I was much too rough and tumble.

Mama had an issue because she always had to mend a hole here or a rip there.

Everyone has that spark.

If it's lit, it can catapult you to heights you never dreamed of.

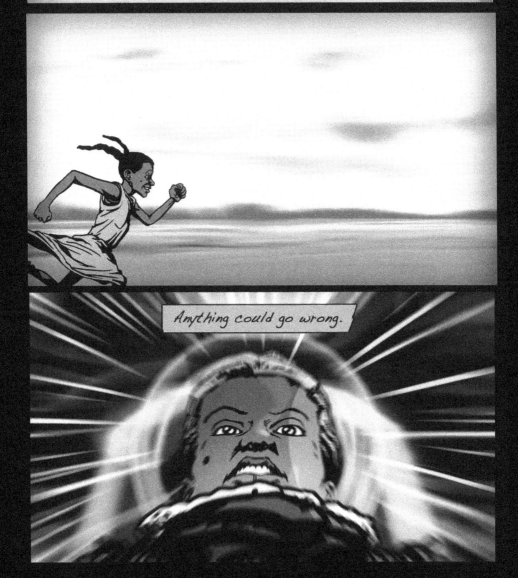

Gravity pressed heavy against my chest- making it hard to breathe.

But my training kicked in. I held that prop steady.

His presence, albeit brief, would be that catalyst in my life.

I would learn to fly.

All I could do was hold on for dear life.

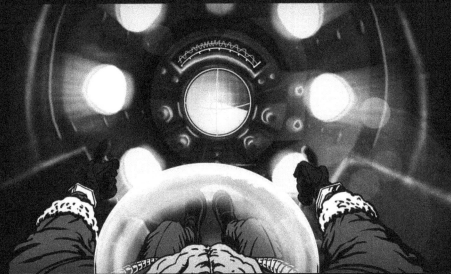

I was gonna find him...

STELLAR
UNION

THE UPPER TROPOSPHERE
1938

Gravity weighed down on me like a tractor.
As long as I took deeper breaths, I'd be okay.

Hunting for a meal was considered ' Men's work.'

Not having a son after two attempts...

Daddy finally took it upon himself to teach his little girl to shoot.

Sensing my hesitance...

...Daddy did what he always did.

He demonstrated a lesson of compassion and courage.

Like a bat outta hell, that rabbit was gone.

I had very good parents. They were a team.

Mama was the Disciplinarian; Daddy was the Dreamer.

My first license was a Class A1-B.

Approaching Target.

I could fly private craft and small industrial frigates.

We'd "look at the radio." That's what we called it.
Daddy built ours back when they were hard to come
by. Daddy rarely talked about what he did in WWI.

He was always
tinkering
with something.

We heard radio plays and music every night.

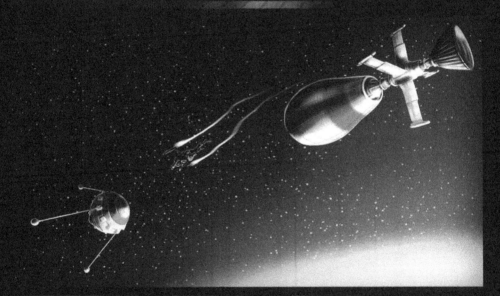

This was us being together as a family.

That dang rock nearly tore my head off!

I had never seen Mama more frightened...

...or Daddy more ANGRY!

YES, I was scared, just as I'm sure Daddy was.

But I had NO FEAR.

ROCKET ACTION! THRILLING

CAPTAIN BATTLE

Flight of the **SHARECROPPER'S SON**

with Paul**Robeson** • Lena**Horne**

Herb**Jeffries** • Butterfly**McQueen** • Dooley**Wilson**

DirectedBy**OscarMicheaux** • ProducedBy**BillRobinson** • MusicBy**DukeEllington**

In Space Deluxe Color

a BIGHEAD SCIENTISTS *production*

MATTY'S ROCKET

Unexpected Guests

3

BIGHEAD SCIENTISTS

FIELDER

DIESELFUNK

MATTY'S ROCKET

Chapter 3

UNEXPECTED GUESTS

a BIGHEAD SCIENTISTS *production*

You ever had one of those times where you're really excited about something but you had to hold it in till the job was done...?

Well, this was like that.

Landing that rocket on the platform had me feeling hyper alert. My focus was about adjusting the aptitude and altitude until I came to a stop.

The white robes didn't do much to hide the obvious evil underneath.

The whispering between Mama and Daddy was frantic.

The plan was to hunker down and let those peckerwoods hurl their insults--.

but fight if they tried to rush the door.

I had passed my landing with flying colors.

Which was fortunate because the engine on my old strato-capsule had burnt out.

Only one step remained towards being made official.

The aeronautics notary was a "Friend," who Francois had used before.

That "used before" part had me a little nervous.

You know its the strangest thing...

...after all of the bullying, drunkeness and outright bigotry...

I was officially a class A1-B.

Where to next?
Paris, Off-world or Harlem?
Who are you now?

The truth is Daddy was...taken....from us.
Not killed. Just...Gone.
Gone...like that Rabbit.

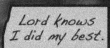

That meant we were in steerage.

COLORED ONLY
No Whites Allowed

But you know me. I heard NO all the time.

I found a way.

I stayed in France for another 18 months to get experience and money under my belt.

I could see the BIG picture.

The next stage had to be done back home.

NEW YORK CITY
1940

I would start an interstellar shipping company..

To do that I was gonna need a bigger Rocket.

To Be Continued...

The power of what some beings call God is vast.

Bigger than the vastness of space in fact.

How arrogant we were thinking we were the center of the Universe.

The crashed ship ruptured the levee that held the great Mississippi River at bay.

How did this happen? Why...why, did this happen? An Act of GOD?

Turns out...what was common as a cold to US, was LETHAL to them.

In defense, Mother Nature had taken back the land. Wiping out homes, families, communities and aliens alike.

Mama and I were sure we were going to die.

The house barely stood against the flooding waters. But it stood all the same.

It was a herculean feat for Mama to get herself and me to the roof... while also giving birth.

My brother, George Watty Jr. was born prematurely in the early am.

AFTERWORD

Mae Jemison was born in 1956 in Decatur, Alabama. A Star Trek fan who adored Uhura, she, too would move to Chicago with her family. While a student at Stanford University, she was president of the Black Student Union and a choreographer. She earned degrees in Chemical Engineering and African American History. Then she went to medical school.

Fluent in several languages, Jemison joined the Peace Corps and served as a medical officer in African nations. After running a private practice as a doctor, she applied for NASA's Astronaut program. On September 12, 1987, she went into space as a mission specialist, becoming the first African American woman to go beyond the stratosphere. (The honors of first Black person and Latino to go into space goes to Arnaldo Tamayo Mendez of Cuba, the first African American in space was Guion Bluford, and the first African American astronaut was Robert Henry Lawrence) Today, Jemison leads the 100 Year Starship Project, a research project to ensure humans can travel to another star within a century.

However, some images of Matty are reminiscent of abolitionist Harriet Tubman. Tubman, a former enslaved woman in the Antebellum South, who freed herself from bondage and returned to the dreaded Southern plantations countless times to help others escape, too. She's known as the greatest of all the "conductors of the Underground Railroad," leading covert missions to help escapees navigate dangerous treks of forests often with bounty hunters on their tail. During the American Civil War, she worked for the Union army as a scout, likely one of the only women to do so. Her greatest feat was leading the Combahee River Raid where she along with her team securing the freedom of 700 enslaved Africans. Harriet was born before airplanes or spaceflight, but she, too, following a distant star.

Creator Tim Fielder says that Matty reminds him of the women who raised him. Matty's grace is much like that of his grandmothers, Helen Lott and Ruby Young. The character's namesake is Tim's great grandmother, Matty Watty, a Choctaw woman of Mississippi. Matty also shares a middle name with Tim's godmother, Myrna Deloris Bain. In some ways, Matty captures the fortitude of Tim's mother, educator Rowena Fielder. These women are elegant women of strength in the rural South. Women known for their problem solving abilities, their sense of responsibility, and their endearing love.

As for Matty's look, we can credit the beauty and talent of Nichelle Nichols, the actress who first played the groundbreaking character, Uhura and "in real life" recruited women applicants for NASA's astronaut program. Nichols was Tim's visual muse.

Matty is inspired by real life superheroes, women who "found a way out of no way" and seized dreams beyond the reach of their peers. Their achievements are stunning, the adversity daunting, but their vision was clear.

Matty's Rocket is for those who didn't have Black heroines gracing their comic book pages but knew them nonetheless. This comic is for those who push past adversity to be the hero of their dreams. This comic is a reminder that there's victory in "getting back up again." Matty's story is for you.

Ytasha L. Womack is a filmmaker, independent scholar, and author. Her books include: Afrofuturism: The World of Black Sci Fi & Fantasy Culture, and the upcoming graphic novel Blak Kube.

"Matty's Rocket" is a concept that goes back to the early to mid-90s. I had finished a series of comic books that taught me different lessons as an artist. A self-published work, 'Death Comes In Fours,' was rushed to successfully make a deadline. As a result, the work wasn't very good. Afterwards, I went to Marvel and did the graphic novel, 'Dr. Dre: Man With A Cold Cold Heart.' That book was great. But through some crazy set of circumstances, allegedly involving the breaking of house arrest and Marvel declaring bankruptcy, that work remains unpublished. The lessons learned: whatever project you do, do not sacrifice quality at the altar of speed, particularly if it's your own work. It was then that I came up with the concept of a black woman in a world strikingly similar to Fritz Lang's 'Metropolis' and 'Buck Rogers.' The title was 'If God Was A Woman.' A DC comics editor, Lou Stathis, seemed to take a liking to the concept. Sadly, Lou passed away before major work could be done. I re-envisioned it again as a daily comic strip that my good friend, Barbara Brandon-Croft, suggested I turn in for King Features. By that time, I had run out of creative gas and the comic book industry was in a death spiral. By the turn of the century, I moved on to animation.

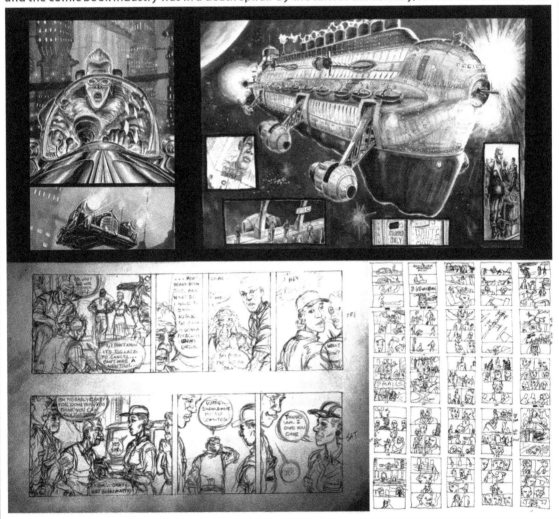

Tim Fielder is an Illustrator, concept designer, cartoonist, and animator born in Tupelo, Mississippi, and raised in Clarksdale, Mississippi. He has a lifelong love of Visual Afrofutuism, Pulp entertainment, and action films. He holds other Afrofuturists such as Samuel R Delany, Octavia Butler, Pedro Bell, and Overton Lloyd as major influences.

Tim makes his empty nest with his wife in the rapidly gentrifying neighborhood of Harlem.

Other books by Tim Fielder:

INFINITUM: An Afrofuturist Tale

Black Metropolis: 30 Years of Afrofuturism, Comics, Music, Animation, Decapitated Chickens, Heroes, Villains, and Negroes.

PHOTO: ED MARSHALL PHOTOGRAPHY

CPSIA information can be obtained
at www.ICGtesting.com
Printed in the USA
LVHW072340140422
716287LV00003B/36

MATTY'S ROCKET

BOOK ONE

DIESELFUNK

MATTY'S ROCKET

Ready For Blastoff!

1

BIGHEAD SCIENTISTS

FIELDER

DIESELFUNK

MANHATTAN
1968

MS. WATTY?

MS. WATTY?...

COAHOMA COUNTY, MISSISSIPPI
1920

I was first born Matty Delores Watty in a rickety cabin with green paint.

I remember the paint because it would chip off and scatter all over the yard.

You could almost say I was born twice in life.

I lived the life that many children of the Jim Crow South lived. Our elders made sure we knew the rules.

But still, we had our pleasures that only youthful ignorance could provide.

I could'nt get the required license and training to fly rockets stateside.

Not one to take no for an answer, I found passage to a country that wouldn't let skin color get in the way.

Francois helped me to find this rocket for a relatively cheap price.

With most of my savings blown, it felt like I spent a mint.

I'll never forget the rocket I took up for my test.

It was at this moment that I was reborn—
like a Phoenix or something.

6, 5, 4,...

CPSIA information can be obtained
at www.ICGtesting.com
Printed in the USA
LVHW072340140422
716287LV00003B/36